Book 9

He Likes

She Likes

by John Shefelbine
Illustrated by Vincent Andriani

SCHOLASTIC

He likes the .

lion

She likes the .

lion

He likes the .

light

She likes the .

light

He likes the [ladder].

She likes the [ladder].

6

He and she like to and .

laugh   laugh

My Words

* to

*new high frequency words